Core Knowledge Language Arts®

Kids Excel
Unit 3 Reader

Skills Strand
GRADE 2

Amplify learning.

Core Knowledge®

ISBN 978-1-61700-209-0

Printed in the USA
NA05 LSCOW 2017

Table of Contents
Kids Excel
Unit 3 Reader

A Letter from the Publisher

Kids,

My name is Mark Deeds, and I have a fun job. I visit with kids who *excel* at what they do.

When you *excel* at something, you are good at it.

The kids I visit all excel at different things. Some of them excel at sports like running or jumping.

Some of them excel at math. Some of them excel at skipping rocks or standing on their hands. All of them are good at something.

I visit with the kids. I chat with them. I ask them how they got started doing what they do and how they got good at it. Sometimes I chat with their moms and dads, too. I jot down notes and take snapshots. Then I write up what they tell me so I can share it with you.

In *Kids Excel* you will meet a lot of kids who excel. I had fun meeting them. I think you will like meeting them, too.

When I meet someone who excels at something, it inspires me to be as good as I can be. I hope the kids in *Kids Excel* have the same effect on you, too!

Mark Deeds

Publisher
Kids Excel

The Spelling Bee

This past spring I went to see the state spelling bee.

The state spelling bee is a spelling contest that lasts two days. On Day 1, a bunch of kids sit down to take a written spelling test. On Day 2, the kids who do the best on the written test get up on a stage and spell.

One hundred ten kids took the spelling test last spring. The kids had to spell words like *chimpanzee*. The 50 who did the best on the written test went on to Day 2 of the spelling bee.

Day 2 is the part of the bee I like best. That's when the kids get up on stage and spell words out loud.

A man will say a word. Then the speller has to spell the word one letter at a time. If the speller spells the word without a mistake, he or she gets to keep spelling. If the speller makes a mistake, a bell rings.

Ding!

Once the bell rings, that is the end. The speller is out of the bee. He or she must sit down in a chair and look on while the rest of the spellers stay in the bee and keep spelling.

On Day 2 of the bee I sat and looked on as the bell rang for lots of kids in the bee.

Airplane. A-e-r-p-l-a-n-e? *Ding!*

Graying. G-r-a-i-n-g? *Ding!*

Sunday. S-u-n-n-d-a-y? *Ding!*

Nate Griffin   Craig Ping   Gail Day

The bell went on ringing all day, until there were just three spellers left.

Nate Griffin, age 12, was one of the three. He was the runner-up at the last spelling bee. Two of the experts I spoke with said they expected him to win the bee.

Craig Ping, age 12, was still in the hunt, too. He had finished in fifth place at the last bee. The experts I spoke with said he had a good chance of winning.

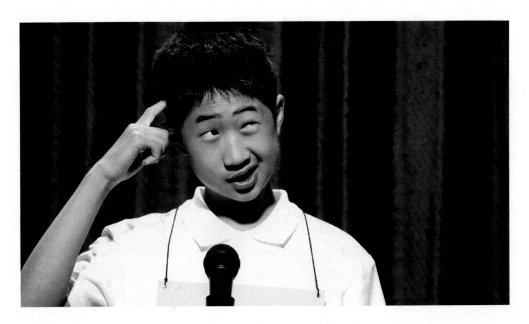

Craig Ping's last stand

Gail Day, age 11, was the dark horse. When I asked the spelling experts who she was, they just shrugged.

Craig Ping was spelling well. Then he got a hard word. He stood thinking. He spelled the word as well as he could. He waited.

Ding!

Craig Ping was out of the bee. That left just Gail Day and Nate Griffin. 🏆

And Then There Were Two

Nate Griffin spelling in the air

Nate Griffin and Gail Day were the last two spellers in the state spelling bee. Mister Griffin was spelling like a champ. But Miss Day was in fine form, too.

Mister Griffin was given a word to spell. He spelled the word in the air with his finger. Then he spelled it out loud.

Gail Day thinking

Miss Day was next. She was given a fifteen-letter word to spell. She had to stop and think a bit. Then she spelled it without a problem.

That's the way it went. Mister Griffin spelled a word. Then Miss Day spelled one. Griffin, Day. Griffin, Day. Back and forth. Back and forth.

Nate Griffin pondering the spelling of penicillin

Nate Griffin wincing after misspelling penicillin

Mister Griffin went word-for-word and letter-for-letter with Miss Day for ten words, until, at last, he was given the word *penicillin*. He tugged on his lip and shifted from foot to foot. He stood there thinking. Time went by. At last he took a shot at spelling the word.

He spelled it: *p-e-n-i-c-i-l-i-n.* (He left out one 'l'.)

Ding! The bell rang.

Mister Griffin was upset. He clenched his hand and winced.

Nate Griffin's slip-up gave Gail Day a shot at winning the spelling bee. She would have to spell *penicillin*. Then she would have to spell one last word.

Miss Day took aim and spelled: *p-e-n-i-c-i-l-l-i-n.*

No bell rang.

The last word was *anesthetic.*

Miss Day stood thinking. Then she spelled: *a-n-e-s-t-h-e-t-i-c.*

No bell rang. Gail Day was the winner!

Mister Griffin was the runner-up, just as he was at the last bee. You could see that he was let down by the loss. But he was a good sport. He went up to Miss Day, shook her hand, and gave her a hug.

Then Gail Day stood on the stage by herself. They gave her a prize. They gave her a check for five hundred bucks. She slipped the check in her pocket and held up the prize.

She was the queen of the bee! 🏆

Gail Day smiles with her prize.

Born to Spell?

How did Gail Day get to be so good at spelling?

Was she born to spell?

Were her parents spelling champs? Did they start training Gail to spell when she was just a babe?

Nope.

I went to West Beach to meet Gail and her parents a week after the bee. Gail's parents met me in the driveway.

The Day home is in West Beach.

Gail's mom, Karen Day, is an artist who paints and works with clay. Gail's dad, David Day, drives a truck. They are as nice a pair as you will ever meet. But they are not spelling champs.

"Spelling was not my best subject," Karen explained as we sat in the living room of the house she and David rent on Davis Street in West Beach.

"I was not bad at spelling," she added, "but I was not the best in my class."

David Day broke into a big grin. "Let's just say I'm not a spelling champ like Gail! It seems like she never makes a mistake!"

Gail's dad, David Day

Karen and Gail smiled.

Karen whispered to me, "When we were dating, David used to write me notes. They were so cute, but there were some spelling mistakes in them."

"When could you tell Gail was a hot shot at spelling?" I asked.

"Well," David said, "I could tell she was good at it, but I did not see just how good she was for a long time. Shucks, I am so proud of her!"

Gail's mom, Karen Day

"When I look back on it," Karen Day said, "it seems to me it all started in second grade, when Gail was in Miss Baker's class."

Gail nodded and said, "It was Miss Baker who got me started. Miss Baker was the best!" 🏆

Miss Baker

I was sitting with spelling champ Gail Day.

I asked her, "How did this Miss Baker make you into a good speller?"

"Well," said Gail, "Miss Baker had a cool way of explaining English spelling. She made spelling trees."

"Spelling trees?"

"Yes," said Gail. "Here, I'll make one for you."

Gail got a sheet of paper and made a tree.

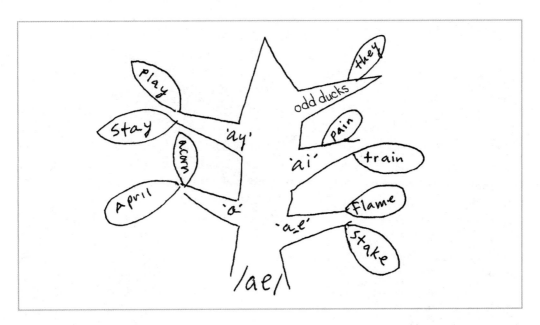

A spelling tree for /ae/

She pointed at the trunk of the tree and explained, "The trunk stands for a sound, like the sound /ae/ as in *cake*. The branches stand for the spellings for that sound. There's one branch for words with the 'a_e' spelling like *flame* and *stake*. There's one branch for words that have the 'ay' spelling like *play* and *stay*. There's one branch for words that have the 'ai' spelling like *pain* and *train*. And so on. Get it?"

"Got it."

"So Miss Baker would make a big spelling tree for a sound. Then we kids would add words to it. When we found words with the sound in them we would stick the words on the branches of the tree. We would stick all of the words with the 'ai' spelling on this branch. We would stick all of the words with the 'ay' spelling on that branch."

"I see. And this helped you get better at spelling?"

Gail nodded.

"The spelling trees helped us see the patterns and keep track of the spellings. They helped us see which spellings are used a lot and which ones are used less. There were a lot of good spellers in Miss Baker's class."

"But not all of them went on to win the state spelling bee," I said. "Why did you?"

Gail shrugged.

"I was good at spelling. But I did not understand why English spelling was so hard. Once I asked Miss Baker why it was so hard. 'Miss Baker,' I said, 'why are there five or six spellings for some sounds? That makes no sense. Why isn't there just one spelling for a sound?'"

Miss Baker explained as much as she could. Then she gave me a book on spelling. It was a cool book. It explained how English has taken in lots of spellings from French, Latin, Greek, and Spanish. When I finished that book, Miss Baker gave me a longer book. Then I found the next book by myself. One book sort of led to the next. So that's how I got started." 🏆

The Swimming Sisters

Kim Castro   Val Castro

Kim and Val Castro are swimming sisters.

Kim is sixteen. Val is fifteen. The sisters swim for the Red River Swim Program (RRSP). Both of them are fast. In fact, they are two of the fastest swimmers in the state.

I went to see the two sisters at the pool where they swim. They were training for a big meet.

"So," I said, "do I dare ask which of you is faster?"

Kim smiled. "I am faster in the sprints," she said. "But Val is faster in the long races."

"So what counts as a sprint in swimming?"

"The 50 Free is a sprint," said Kim.

"50?" I said. "Is that 50 feet?"

"No," said Kim, "it's 50 yards."

"Gosh!" I said. "50 yards? That's a sprint? It sounds long to me! You see, I am not much of a swimmer."

"The 50 Free is an all-out sprint," Kim said. "It's like the hundred yard dash in track. It's over in a flash. The 100 Free is a sprint, too."

"So what counts as a long race in swimming?"

"The 500 Free is a long race," Kim groaned. "It's too long for me. I start to get tired after 150 yards or so. But not Val! The longer the race is, the better she is."

"The 500 Free is my best race!" said Val.

"500 yards?" I said. "What's that, a hundred laps?"

"Um, no," Val said. "In a 25-yard pool, it's up and back ten times."

I jotted notes in my notebook.

"So let's see," I said. "100 yards counts as a short race. Kim is good at the short races. 500 yards is a long race. Val is good at the long races. Is there a race that is longer than 100 yards and shorter than 500?"

"Yes, there is," said Kim. "The 200 Free."

"So which of you speedsters wins that race?" I asked.

Kim looked at Val. She had a smile on her face. It was a sister-to-sister smile, and there was something else in it. There was a sort of challenge in the look.

Val smiled back. She had the same look on her face.

I waited.

At last Kim spoke. "It's hard to say who is faster in the 200 Free. Sometimes Val wins and sometimes I win."

"I see," I said. "It sounds like the 200 Free is the race to see. When will that race take place?"

"It will be on Sunday," said Val, "the last day of the state meet."

I got out my pen and wrote: "Sunday the 25th. 200 Free. Castro versus Castro!"

Val's Training

Val Castro   Coach Pibwell

After I met with Kim and Val, both sisters jumped in the pool and started swimming. Kim jumped in Lane 3. Val jumped in Lane 9.

"Why don't they both swim in the same lane?" I asked RRSP coach, Stan Pibwell.

"They don't have the same training program," Coach Pibwell explained. "Kim is a sprinter. Val swims the longer races, like the 500. The races are not the same, so the training is not the same."

Val swimming

We stood next to Lane 9, where Val was swimming. She swam back and forth, back and forth, back and forth.

"When will she get to stop?" I asked.

"Not for a while," said the coach. "Val is training hard for the big meet. She has been swimming a lot of yards. In a week or so she will start to swim less so that her arms and legs feel loose and rested for the big meet. But it's not time for her to taper off yet. This morning she has a lot of yards to swim."

"Do I dare ask what counts as a lot?"

"She's been swimming 7,000 or 8,000 yards a day," said the coach.

"Yikes!" I said. "That's like five miles!"

"Yep," said Coach Pibwell. "That's what it takes to be the best."

"When she finishes swimming, will she get to go home and sleep?"

"Nope! Later on, after she gets out of the pool, she will do bench presses and leg presses. She will do sit-ups and chin-ups."

"Oh man," I moaned. "It makes me tired just to hear all of that!"

"It's like they say: there's no gain without pain!" said Coach Pibwell. 🏆

Coach Stan Pibwell smiles at the swimmers.

Kim's Training

After seeing Val train, I went to Lanes 3–5, where Kim and the rest of the sprinters were training. They were not swimming lap after lap like Val. They were practicing their starts.

"Swimmers, take your marks!" a coach yelled.

Kim and the rest of the sprinters bent down. They grabbed the starting blocks with their fingers.

"Hup!" yelled the coach.

The sprinters exploded off the blocks. They dove into the pool. Kim was the fastest off the blocks. She sprang like a cat. Her hands seemed to make a hole in the pool. Then her arms and her legs went in the same hole.

Kim went under. She started kicking with her legs like a fish. Then she popped up and started swimming. She took five fast strokes. Then she stopped. She swam to the side of the pool, got out, and went back to the starting blocks.

"Why did she stop?" I asked.

"We are just practicing the start," said Coach Pibwell. "You see, the start is a big thing in a sprint like the 50 Free. If you are fast off the starting blocks, you have a good chance of winning the race. But if you trail off the blocks, it's hard to win. You end up back in the waves, getting sloshed from side to side. That's why we have the sprinters do lots of starts. Kim's start has been getting better and better."

"So, Coach," I said, "do you think Kim can win the 50 Free at the state meet?"

"She should win it," said the coach. "I think she is the best overall swimmer in the state. Plus, as you can see, she has a strong start. But the 50 Free is so fast. A lot of swimmers could win it."

Kim Castro excels in the sprint races.

"And the 100 Free?"

"She should win that, too."

"And the 200?" I asked.

Coach Pibwell smiled.

"Well," he said, "the 200 Free should be one heck of a race. Kim could win all three, the 50, the 100, and the 200. That's her goal. But Val will be swimming that race, too."

Coach Pibwell looked to see if Kim was looking. She was not. Then he whispered, "I think Val gets a kick out of swimming faster than her big sister. And she has been training hard. The 200 is like a short jog for her. So it should be a good race!"

I got out my notebook. I looked at the page where I had written: "Sunday the 25th. 200 Free. Castro versus Castro!" I underlined it twice. 🏆

The Big Race

I got to the pool in time for the 200 Free. I sat in the stands with Grover and Joan Castro, Kim and Val's parents.

"I am so proud of Kim and Val," said Grover Castro. "But I have a bad case of nerves. I hate it when the two of them swim in the same race. They have both been training so hard. They would both like to win this race. But they can't both win. I don't like to think that one of them may be upset."

A man's booming voice filled the air. "It's time for the last race of the meet!" the man said.

Fans clap for the Castro sisters.

"Let's meet our swimmers!" The man started listing the swimmers in the race.

"In Lane 2," he said, "from Red River Swim Program, we have the winner of the 500 Free, Val Castro." Cheers rose up from the RRSP swimmers on the deck and from fans in the stands.

"In Lane 3," the man said, "from Red River Swim Program, the winner of the 50 and 100 Free, Kim Castro." There were shouts and cheers for Kim, as well.

The swimmers got up on the starting blocks.

A man in a white coat said, "Swimmers, take your marks." The swimmers bent down and grabbed the starting blocks.

Then there was a beep. The swimmers shot off. Kim's start was perfect. She did her kick. Then she popped up and started swimming. Her arms went so fast. She seemed to be coasting.

Kim was the fastest swimmer for a hundred yards.

She made a big wave. The rest of the swimmers were trailing her. They seemed to be bouncing and sloshing in Kim's waves.

I was starting to think it would not be such a close race after all. But just as I was thinking this, Grover Castro said, "Wait for it!"

"Wait for what?" I said.

"You'll see!" said Grover.

I looked back at the pool. Kim was still winning. But Val was closing in on her. The gap was five feet. Then it was three.

The swimmers flipped one last time. Kim was starting to look a bit tired. The gap was down to two feet. Then it was one foot. Then the two sisters were swimming side by side. As they came to the finish line it was too close to pick a winner. Kim and Val smacked the side of the pool at what looked to be the same moment.

A hundred parents in the stands looked up at the clock. A hundred swimmers on the deck looked up as well.

This is what the clock said:

Val Castro   Lane 2 1:45

Kim Castro   Lane 3 1:46

Val was the winner! 🏆

Kim Castro (on the left) smiles at her sister, Val, after Val's win in the 200 Free.

The Soccer Twins, Part I

I was standing on the sidelines while the Clark Bees got set to play their last soccer game of the year. The Clark team had racked up sixteen wins without a loss. They had just one game left to play. They were getting set to play the Dickens Chargers.

Les and Pat Pinker

The Clark team has two team leaders this year who happen to be twin sisters. Their names are Les and Pat Pinker. As I stood on the sidelines, I spoke with the twins' dad, Ted Pinker. He was holding the Pinkers' dog, Princess, on a leash.

"Which one is Les?" I asked.

"That one," said Ted Pinker, pointing.

Ted Pinker explained that Les plays wing. Her job is to take shots on the goal. Les is a fast runner. She is good at passing the ball, too.

Les came to the sidelines to visit with us. We shook hands. I asked her, "Let's say you could offer just one tip to kids who would like to be better at soccer. What would you tell them?"

Les said, "I think I would tell them to get good at passing. If a team can't pass well, it will never get good shots on goal. You have to get so good at passing that you do not have to think what your feet are doing. Your feet just sort of think for themselves."

Les petted Princess and ran off. I went to chat with her twin sister, Pat. Pat is the goalkeeper for the team. It's her job to stop shots and keep players from scoring on the Clark goal.

When we spotted her, Pat was slipping on mitts. She explained, "Without these mitts, my hands would get red. I would get blisters. Plus, the mitts help me get a grip on the ball.

"What's the best tip for stopping a shot?" I asked.

"Well," Pat said, "You need to have soft hands."

"Soft hands?" I said. "You mean you have to use a lot of hand cream?"

Pat grinned. "No, what I mean is that your hands need to bend back when the ball hits them. They need to bend so they can take the shock. If they don't bend, the ball will bounce off your hands and then you will have to get set to stop the next shot. It's better to catch the ball if you can, or knock it out of bounds."

Just then a buzzer went off. It was time for the big game. 🏆

The Soccer Twins, Part II

Les and Pat ran off to play in their big game. Their dog, Princess, tugged on the leash, hoping she could play, as well. Ted held her back. He petted Princess and got her to sit on the sidelines.

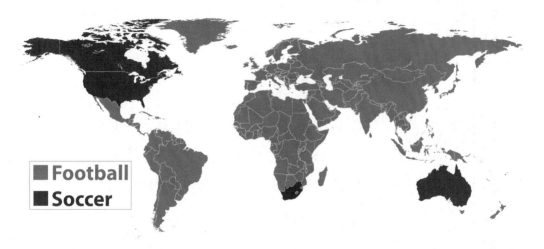

Football
Soccer

We looked on as Les and Pat played soccer. We say soccer here in the United States But outside of the United States, they say *football*. The name *football* makes a lot of sense since the players use their feet to kick the ball. The goalkeeper can use her hands to stop the ball, but the rest of the players can't use their hands. But maybe an even better name would be *feetball*. After all, you use both feet. *Soccer*, *football*, or *feetball*—which name do you think is best?

At one point Les made a nice pass. Her teammate had a shot on goal. She kicked the ball hard, but it bounced off the goalpost.

Pat played well, too. She had to block two shots by the Dickens players. She knocked one out of bounds and grabbed one with her mitts.

Both teams had shots on goal, but for a long time there was no scoring. The clock ticked down. It started to look like the game would end in a 0-0 tie. Then Les got the ball. She passed to a teammate. The teammate ran a bit and then passed the ball back to Les. Les took a shot. The ball went zipping past the Dickens goalkeeper and into the net!

Goal! The Clark Bees ran and jumped on top of Les. Clark was in the lead, but there was still time left in the game.

The Dickens players got the ball back. They ran and passed the ball. A Dickens player took a shot, but Pat grabbed it. Just then the horn went off. The game was over!

The Clark Bees were the winners. They were the state soccer champs! 🏆

Jump!

Drive down Tenth Street in the summer and you will see them—the jumpers. You will see kids jumping rope on playgrounds and street corners.

Jumping rope is something lots of kids like to do. But most kids are not as good at it as the Jumping Stars.

The last time I met with the Jumping Stars was in August. They were jumping at the playground where they hang out. Two of them were spinning the rope. Two of them were jumping over the rope as it spun past. The rope was spinning so fast it was hard to see it. The jumpers' feet went *pit-pat-pit-pat-pit-pat* on the blacktop.

This sport is named jumping rope. But that makes it sound much less cool than it is. The kids don't just jump. They dance. They twist and spin. They hop and skip. They flip. They land on their hands and then pop back up on their feet. They do all of this while jumping over a rope at top speed. It is an art form, like dancing.

Kit Winter

Jo Palmer

There are four jumpers on the Jumping Stars, Kit Winter, Jo Palmer, Kate Agee, and Jaylin Smith. Kit and Jo are the top jumpers.

Kit is sixteen. She is an awesome jumper. She has been jumping rope since she was five. She is also one of the most cheerful kids I know. Kit has a great smile. She is always quiet. She always keeps her cool. I have never seen her get mad.

Jo is something else. She jumps like a goddess, and sometimes she acts like one, too. She plans the tricks they do. She says who goes where. She is the boss.

Kate Agee   *Jaylin Smith*

The day I visited, the Jumping Stars were practicing a trick Jo had made up for herself and Kit. It was called the flip. When the Stars do the flip, Jo starts out jumping next to Kit. Then she draws near to Kit. Then she flips over Kit's back and lands on the far side. Both of them keep jumping all the while. It's a cool trick.

I looked on as the kids did the flip six times. Three times they nailed it. Three times they missed it.

You could see Jo was upset when she and Kit muffed the trick. Jo would moan and groan. She would cross her arms and sulk. Jo would set her hands on her hips like a mom who is mad at her kids. But Jo was mad at herself, so she went and sat on the lawn.

After a bit, the Jumping Stars paused for a rest. That gave me a chance to chat with them.

"There's a big jumping contest next week," Kit explained.

"Think you can win it?" I asked.

"I hope so," said Kit. "Last time we were seventh."

"Nice job!" I said.

"Seventh is not good!" Jo said. Kit and the rest of the Jumping Stars nodded. But they did not seem to feel the pain of seventh place quite as much as Jo.

"That flip you were practicing—will you be doing that one in the meet?"

"I hope so," said Jo. "We need to get good at it. We need to get to the point where we nail it nine times out of ten."

Then Jo said to her teammates, "Let's do it! We are going to keep practicing from dawn until dusk, until we can do the flip in our sleep!" 🏆

The Dispute

I could not make it to the jump rope contest. I had to go to a wedding. But I told Jo and Kit I would speak to them after it was over to see how the Jumping Stars did.

But that is not what happened. They rang me.

"Mark?" Kit said. "Hey, it's Kit Winter."

"Hey, Kit! How did it go?"

"Well, not quite as well as we had hoped," said Kit. "We made it to the last round, but when we did the flip, we sort of muffed it when my foot got caught in the rope."

"Aw," I said, "that's too bad. What place did you get?"

"Fifth."

"Fifth? Fifth is good, Kit! That's two spots better than last time!"

"Well," Kit said, "don't tell Jo that fifth place is cool. She's here, and she wants to tell you something."

Jo got on the line.

"Fifth is no good!" she said. "We need to keep practicing. We need to do better tricks. I need to land the flip!"

Jo

This is classic Jo. She is intense and hard on herself. She always wants to be better.

Jo went on. "It's a bummer. But I felt like we had to tell you that we can't be in *Kids Excel* after all."

"Why not?"

"Fifth place is not bad—but not bad is not the same as excelling," said Jo.

"I think fifth place is good. I think you told me there were a hundred jumping squads in the contest."

"One hundred and ten," said Jo. "But still, fifth stinks. We can do better! And when we do, then you can run something on us in *Kids Excel*. But not until then."

I had to smile.

"Hey, Jo," I said, "you are not the boss of me! *Kids Excel* is my mag. I get to say who gets to be in it. I happen to think that you and Kit and the rest of the Jumping Stars *do* excel."

"Please don't run a profile of us yet!" Jo said. "*Wait until we excel!*"

"I'll think it over," I said.

Jo hung up.

I did think things over. I think that Jo and Kit and the Jumping Stars are cool. I don't care that they came in fifth place. Jo is awesome, and they all train so hard, that I bet they will not be in fifth place the next time they enter a contest.

So here they are—the Jumping Stars!

(Jo Palmer, if you are looking at this, don't be upset at me. I can tell when kids excel. It's my job!) 🏆

The Jumping Stars

The Splash Artist

When Jethro Otter jumps into his pool, a wave jumps out. Or rather, it is driven out by the force of Jethro landing. You see, Jethro is a *splash artist.*

"For a long time my nickname was *The Splash King*," Jethro explained as I sat with him and his dad on the deck in their backyard.

"But then I switched it to *The Splash Artist*," said his dad.

"Why the switch?" I asked.

"Well, you see," said Jethro's dad, "Jethro is not just good at making a big splash. He can also make the splash shoot this way or that. He can pick a target and hit it within a foot or two. If you ask me, it's an art form. And that's why I gave him the nickname *The Splash Artist*."

"Wait a minute!" I said. "Are you saying that if you and I pick a target, he can jump in the pool and make the splash hit the target?"

"Yep—as long as it's in his splashing reach."

"I would like to see that!" I said.

"Will do!" said Jethro. "Which bed do you want me to hit, Dad?"

Bed of Lettuce

"Um, why don't you hit the one with the green peppers," said his dad.

"No problem," said Jethro. He went to the pool house to get his swim trunks.

While Jethro was getting his swim trunks, his dad and I looked at the yard. He pointed out some some shrubs, a wooden trellis, and a set of garden beds he had planted on one side of the pool. The garden beds were filled with lots of lettuce, peppers, and eggplants.

Jethro's dad pointed out that the green peppers

Jethro's Dad

in one of the beds looked a bit wilted. "It was hot the past two days," he said. "The peppers could use a splash."

Jethro came out of the pool house with his trunks on.

"We had better step back a bit," said Jethro's dad, "unless you are in the mood to get wet."

We took five big steps back.

Jethro went out to the pool. His two sisters were floating on pool rafts. One of them was sipping a drink. They did not see Jethro. Jethro snuck up on them. He bounced once. He bounced twice. That was when his sisters spotted him. They shouted and went to the end of the pool. But they were not Jethro's target.

At the last moment, Jethro grabbed one knee. Then he tilted himself back, and jumped so his back hit the pool. A great wave rose out of the pool and arched into the air. It rose up and came crashing down, like a cat pouncing on a mouse. His sisters winced, thinking the wave would land on them. But it did not hit them. It landed, just as Jethro had said it would, on the garden bed with the green peppers.

"Nice one!" said Jethro's dad. "That should keep those peppers moist!" 🏆

The Art of the Splash

Jethro, also known as *The Splash Artist,* had a lot of splashes that he could do.

He tucked his legs up into his chest and smacked into the pool, sending a splash cascading onto the shrubs. Then he did a "can opener" and sent a big splash onto his sisters. It was a hot day, so they were not too upset.

Jethro splashes his sisters.

When Jethro finished splashing, we sat down to chat.

"So how did you get into splashing?" I asked.

"I have been splashing since I was five or six. You see, Dad and I like to swim. In the summer we are out here by the pool all weekend," said Jethro. "We swim and splash from dawn to dusk. When I was six or seven we started to have splash contests."

"Dad was bigger than me. He still is. So he makes a big splash. I saw that if I wanted to outsplash him, I had to be smart. I found out there is an art to how you land in the pool. If you bend at the moment you hit, that helps a lot. If you hit the pool sort of slanted, you can make a big, big splash. And, best of all, you can target the splash. What matters the most is how your back is facing when you hit. You can bend it and tilt it all sorts of different ways. Once you get the hang of it, you can make the splash shoot off to one side and start aiming at targets, like garden beds, or sisters. Sisters are harder to hit since they can run and swim. Also, sometimes they splash you back."

Jethro grows up.

"How long did it take you to get good at splashing?" I asked.

"It took a long time. I'd say five summers. I made hundreds and hundreds of splashes. Lots of them were lame."

This is something almost all of the kids I meet tell me. Whether they excel at making splashes or spelling words, they all say it takes time to get good. If you want to be good at something, you have to keep at it. If you want to be one of the best, you have to keep at it day in and day out.

Splashman Contest!

3 pm, August 30th
County Pool

Grand Prize:
100 Bucks!

"So you used those tricks to win the big contest?"

"Yep. The Splashman Contest was last week. Dad and I went down for it. On my last splash I landed a nice one. I soaked the deck. All the fans were dripping wet. At the Splashman Contest that's a *good* thing. The fans there *want* to get wet. They think you are awesome if you soak them to the skin. It's not like when you get your sisters wet and they run off to whine to Mom. *Boo, hoo!*"

"It was a great splash," said his dad. "One of the best I've ever seen!"

"What was the prize?" I asked.

"A hundred bucks," said Jethro.

"What are you going to spend it on?"

"Um," Jethro said, "Mom says we have to use it to fill the pool."

Jethro's dad nodded.

"Man, you should see our pool bill!" he said. "We have to fill the pool each day to make up for what Jethro splashes out. A splash here, a splash there. After a while, it starts to add up."

It was getting late. I had jotted down all the facts. It was time for me to go. I shook hands with *The Splash Artist*. Then I went back to my car.

As I drove off, I saw Jethro do one last splash. He sent a huge splash shooting onto one of the garden beds. I think it was the one with the eggplants. 🏆

The Math Contest

There were lots and lots of kids taking the state math test as part of a math contest.

I grabbed a test booklet and a pencil. I sat down.

This is what I saw in the test booklet:

Problem 1. Three runners are running a ten-mile race. Runner 1 runs a mile in six minutes. Runner 2 runs a mile in seven minutes. Runner 3 runs a mile in ten minutes. After five miles, Runner 1 and Runner 2 sit down to have lunch. Runner 1 spends fifteen minutes eating her lunch. Runner 2 spends ten minutes eating her lunch. Runner 3 keeps running. Who wins the race?

A lot of time has passed since I took a math class. I had to sit and think. It took me ten minutes, but in the end I did get Problem 1. (Runner 1 wins.)

After I did Problem 1, I was feeling proud of myself. Then I looked at the kids sitting next to me. They had finished lots of problems in the time it had taken me to do one. One of them was on Problem 10. One was on Problem 15.

The Test

I looked at Problem 2. There were numbers and letters all over the place. You had to add. You had to subtract. You had to divide. You had to take the square root of a number. I kept at it for ten minutes. But I got mixed up. At last I wrote so much that my pencil broke! The problem was just too much for me.

I closed the test booklet and handed it back to Dr. Maud Chang.

"What did you think?" she asked.

Dr. Maud Chang

"I think I didn't do so well," I said. "I did Problem 1, but Problem 2 was too hard for me."

By this point I was not feeling proud of myself. But Dr. Chang was sweet. She smiled and patted me on the back. Then she said, "You should be proud you got one. This is a hard test."

Dr. Chang and I sat down to chat.

"The kids taking the test are sixteen or seventeen," she explained. "There are 60 of them. There are 100 problems on the test."

"Are all of the problems as hard as the two I did?"

Dr. Chang smiled. "Well, yes. The problems get harder and harder as you go on."

"I see!"

So, if Problem 1 and Problem 2 were that hard, then just think of what the rest must be like!

"How much time do the kids get?" I asked.

"180 minutes."

"And who will grade the tests?"

"I will," said Dr. Chang. "We should have the winner's name by the end of next week."

"Good," I said. "Let me know who wins." 🏆

The Winner

Winner Hans Brucker

Dr. Chang texted me the next week. "We have a winner!" she texted. "The winner of the math contest is Hans Brucker!"

I met Hans not long after. We met in his math classroom.

Hans is sixteen. He is Dutch. His mom came with him to the United States when he was twelve. He is blond and thin.

"I am from the Netherlands," Hans said. "My English, sad to say, it is not so good."

Hans works on a math problem.

"Well," I said, "my math is not so good. I could not get past Problem 2 on that test."

"Problem 2?" said Hans. "That was this one, I think."

Hans wrote out the problem.

"Yes," I moaned, "I tried that problem and I lost."

Hans doing the problem that I couldn't do

I watched as Hans started jotting down numbers and letters. He got the problem in less than a minute.

"See?" he said. "It is not so hard!"

"Hans," I said, "Dr. Chang tells me you aced that test. She says you missed just six problems out of a hundred. That is fantastic! Tell me. How did you get so good at math?"

Hans sat down and told me the tale of his life. He spoke good English but with a thick accent.

Hans grows up.

"When I was a kid in the Netherlands, math was the subject I liked best. When I was seven I found that doing math problems was a lot of fun. So I would check out math books and do the problems in them, just for fun."

I jotted down notes.

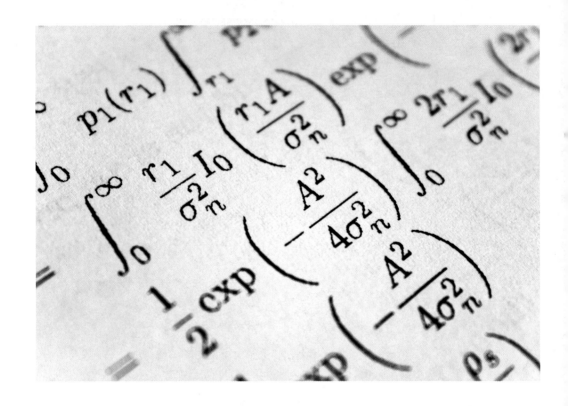

"In life there are some problems you can take care of," Hans explained. "Then there are some problems you can't. But math problems are not like that. If you think hard and stick with it, you can get the math problems."

"Well," I said. "Maybe *you* can! But not all of us can, as I found out last week."

Hans went on, "I never made a plan to get good at math. I just did problems for fun. I did a lot of problems. And after a while I got good at it."

"The test was in English. Did that make it harder for you?"

"I used to think the word problems would be hard, but they were not so bad. I had to translate the words from English into Dutch. But the numbers are the same in English as in Dutch. They look the same on the page, and they stand for the same things. So there is no need to translate. That is part of why I like math so much. It is the same in all places. 3 + 3 = 6 in the Netherlands. It is the same here in the United States. It is the same on the moon, or on Mars!" 🏆

Too Much Mail

I was wrapping up my meeting with Hans Brucker, who happens to be the latest state math champ.

I asked him, "Has winning the state math contest made your life different?"

"Overall, my life is the same," said Hans. "I was in the paper. Then that stopped. The main thing that is different is that I have been getting a lot of mail."

"What sort of mail? Fan mail?"

Yale

"Well, sort of. The mail I am getting is from colleges where math is taught. I got a letter from a college in the United States. The name of the college is Yale. Is Yale a good place to take math classes?"

"I'm not an expert on math, but I'll bet it is," I said.

"Yes? Yale is good? OK, I will . . . what is it you say in English? *I will make a note of that.* But you see, there is a problem."

"What's the problem?" I asked.

"Too much mail! You see, it is not just Yale. I am getting lots of letters. Yesterday I got a letter from a college named Penn State. Last week I got letters from Wisconsin and Cornell. So this is the problem: lots of colleges. They all write to say: 'Pick us! Take a math class with us!' Which one should I pick?"

"Hans," I said, "this is what we call *a good problem to have*. If you think hard and stick with it, I just bet you will get this problem, too!" 🏆

Too much mail

How to Skip a Rock

I was standing by the side of Lake Cayman with ace rock skipper Moe Keller.

Moe, who is eleven, was telling me how to skip a rock.

"For starters," he said, "you have to pick a good rock. You want one that is smooth and flat."

Moe bent down and scooped up some rocks. He held them in his hands for me to see.

A handful of good skipping rocks

"Here are some rocks that are just begging to be skipped! See how nice and flat they are?"

Moe picked one of the rocks. It was small, thin, smooth, and gray. It was two inches from end to end. He held it in his hand so I could see it.

"You want to hold it in your hand, with the flat side down. Wrap the side of the rock with your index finger, like this. Then sling it. It's best to toss sidearm. You don't want to aim it down at the lake too much. You want the rock to be whizzing just inches from the top of the lake. And, as you let go of the rock, you want to snap your wrist so the rock starts spinning."

Moe skips a rock.

I looked on as Moe tossed the rock. It went skittering on the lake. *Pitter-pat, pitter-pat, pitter-pat, pitter-pat.* It must have skipped ten or twelve times.

"You want to skip one?" Moe asked.

It did not look hard when Moe did it. So I bent down and picked up a rock. I wrapped the rock in my finger. Then I flung it sidearm at the lake.

The rock struck the lake and sank. I can't say it sank like a rock since it *was* a rock. The point is, it did not skip.

"When the rock sinks like that, we say it's a *plonk*," said Moe. "That's not what we want to see."

I picked up a rock and tossed it.

Plonk!

"Snap your wrist!" Moe called.

I snapped my wrist as well as I could.

Plonk!

My plonk

"You are so close," said Moe. "Let me help you." He came up to my side and pointed out how to toss the rock.

I tossed the rock. This time it was different. The rock hit the top of the lake and went *pitter-pat*. It was just three skips, but it felt awesome.

"Rock solid!" shouted Moe.

I soon found out that Moe, as a rock-skipper, likes to use the word *rock*. He sticks it in whenever he gets a chance.

I skipped a bunch of rocks. I got one to skip five times.

Moe yelled, "You rock!"

The next rock I tossed skipped six times.

"It's like magic!" I said. "It's cool! I'm hooked!"

Mark's second try

Letting the Ducks Out

As we roamed by the lake, Moe Keller gave me a lesson on rock skipping as a sport.

"What matters?" I asked. "Is it how far the rock skips or the number of times it skips?"

"Well," said Moe, "here in the United States what matters is the number of times the rock skips. But in the United Kingdom it's not like that. Over there what matters is how far the rock goes. Also, over there in the United Kingdom it is not named rock skipping."

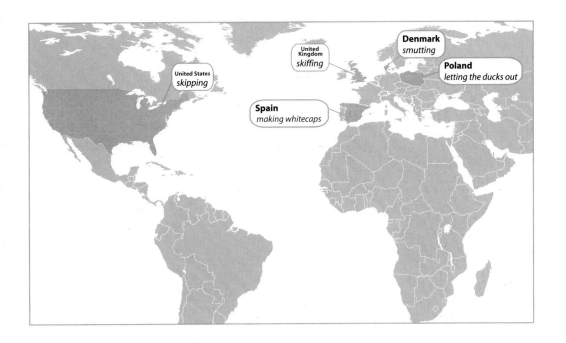

Denmark
smutting

United
Kingdom
skiffing

Poland
letting the ducks out

United States
skipping

Spain
making whitecaps

"What is it named?"

"Stone skiffing."

"Skiffing? I like the sound of that!"

When Moe saw that I liked the word *skiffing*, he reeled off a list of names for skipping rocks. "In Denmark it is named *smutting*. In Spain it's *making whitecaps*. In Poland it's *letting the ducks out*."

"Letting the ducks out? Are you kidding?"

"No joke. That's what they say."

"Why do they say that?"

Moe shrugged, "I'm not sure."

"Let's focus on the number of skips," I said. "What's a good number?"

"15 is not bad. 20 is good. 30 is awesome. The record number of skips ever is 51."

"51? And I was so proud of my six skips!"

"Well," Moe said, "you are just starting out."

"I think you said you went to a stone skiffing contest in the United Kingdom. How did it go? Did you skiff your way to a prize?" I asked.

"I had one great skiff," said Moe. "It landed me in fifth place."

"Out of?"

"Out of a hundred or so skiffers."

"That's so cool!" I said, patting him on the back. "Bravo! That's the way to let the ducks out!"

Moe smiled. "Want to see a snapshot?" he asked.

I nodded.

Moe got out a snapshot of him with his prize.

"My goal for the next trip over there is to be in the top three," he said.

"Rock on!" I said. 🏆

About this Book

This book has been created for use by students learning to read with the Core Knowledge Language Arts. Readability levels are suitable for early readers. The book has also been carefully leveled in terms of its "code load," or the number of spellings used in the stories.

The English writing system is complex. It uses more than 200 spellings to stand for 40-odd sounds. Many sounds can be spelled several different ways, and many spellings can be pronounced several different ways. This book has been designed to make early reading experiences easier and more productive by using a subset of the available spellings. It uses *only* spellings that students have been taught to sound out as part of their phonics lessons, plus a handful of tricky words, which have also been deliberately introduced in the lessons. This means that the stories will be 100% decodable if they are assigned at the proper time.

As the students move through the program, they learn new spellings and the "code load" in the decodable readers increases gradually. The code load graphics on this page indicate the number of spellings students are expected to know in order to read the first story of the book and the number of spellings students are expected to know in order to read the final stories in the book. The columns on the inside back cover list the specific spellings and tricky words students are expected to recognize at the beginning of this reader. The bullets at the bottom of the inside back cover identify spellings, tricky words, and other topics that are introduced gradually in the unit this reader is designed to accompany.

Visit us on the web at www.coreknowledge.org

CORE KNOWLEDGE LANGUAGE ARTS

SERIES EDITOR-IN-CHIEF
E. D. Hirsch, Jr.

PRESIDENT
Linda Bevilacqua

EDITORIAL STAFF
Carolyn Gosse, Senior Editor - Preschool
Khara Turnbull, Materials Development Manager
Michelle L. Warner, Senior Editor - Listening & Learning

Mick Anderson
Robin Blackshire
Maggie Buchanan
Paula Coyner
Sue Fulton
Sara Hunt
Erin Kist
Robin Luecke
Rosie McCormick
Cynthia Peng
Liz Pettit
Ellen Sadler
Deborah Samley
Diane Auger Smith
Sarah Zelinke

DESIGN AND GRAPHICS STAFF
Scott Ritchie, Creative Director

Kim Berrall
Michael Donegan
Liza Greene
Matt Leech
Bridget Moriarty
Lauren Pack

CONSULTING PROJECT MANAGEMENT SERVICES
ScribeConcepts.com

ADDITIONAL CONSULTING SERVICES
Ang Blanchette
Dorrit Green
Carolyn Pinkerton

ACKNOWLEDGMENTS

These materials are the result of the work, advice, and encouragement of numerous individuals over many years. Some of those singled out here already know the depth of our gratitude; others may be surprised to find themselves thanked publicly for help they gave quietly and generously for the sake of the enterprise alone. To helpers named and unnamed we are deeply grateful.

CONTRIBUTORS TO EARLIER VERSIONS OF THESE MATERIALS
Susan B. Albaugh, Kazuko Ashizawa, Nancy Braier, Kathryn M. Cummings, Michelle De Groot, Diana Espinal, Mary E. Forbes, Michael L. Ford, Ted Hirsch, Danielle Knecht, James K. Lee, Diane Henry Leipzig, Martha G. Mack, Liana Mahoney, Isabel McLean, Steve Morrison, Juliane K. Munson, Elizabeth B. Rasmussen, Laura Tortorelli, Rachael L. Shaw, Sivan B. Sherman, Miriam E. Vidaver, Catherine S. Whittington, Jeannette A. Williams

We would like to extend special recognition to Program Directors Matthew Davis and Souzanne Wright who were instrumental to the early development of this program.

SCHOOLS
We are truly grateful to the teachers, students, and administrators of the following schools for their willingness to field test these materials and for their invaluable advice: Capitol View Elementary, Challenge Foundation Academy (IN), Community Academy Public Charter School, Lake Lure Classical Academy, Lepanto Elementary School, New Holland Core Knowledge Academy, Paramount School of Excellence, Pioneer Challenge Foundation Academy, New York City PS 26R (The Carteret School), PS 30X (Wilton School), PS 50X (Clara Barton School), PS 96Q, PS 102X (Joseph O. Loretan), PS 104Q (The Bays Water), PS 214K (Michael Friedsam), PS 223Q (Lyndon B. Johnson School), PS 308K (Clara Cardwell), PS 333Q (Goldie Maple Academy), Sequoyah Elementary School, South Shore Charter Public School, Spartanburg Charter School, Steed Elementary School, Thomas Jefferson Classical Academy, Three Oaks Elementary, West Manor Elementary.

And a special thanks to the CKLA Pilot Coordinators Anita Henderson, Yasmin Lugo-Hernandez, and Susan Smith, whose suggestions and day-to-day support to teachers using these materials in their classrooms was critical.

Core Knowledge®

WRITERS
Matt Davis, Core Knowledge Staff